For Mickey,

from Bob

Christmas 71

Bob W. Bruner

1 John 1:4